To the us

This book is written for the teacher who would value a varied collection of mathematical activities for use in emergency situations.

Each activity provides a challenge for the pupil based on a particular mathematical idea. It is hoped that they will find the work stimulating and enjoyable. Most of the activities can be extended in various directions, and lead to valuable pupil-pupil discussion and pupil-teacher discussion.

Some teachers may wish to use the material more selectively. For example, SHEET 4 will provide support material for work on "angles," SHEET 5 will help pupils learning "multiplication facts", SHEET 31 is a useful activity for consolidating work on "equivalent fractions,"_____and so on.

My hope is that you will find this material a valuable source for creative mathematical activity in your classroom.

Dave Kirkby

© Collins Educational

ISBN 0 00 329487 0

First published in 1989 by Holmes McDougall Ltd., Edinburgh.

This edition published in 1991 by Collins Educational, London and Glasgow.

Reprinted 1994

Printed by Martins The Printers, Berwick upon Tweed.

Draw differently shaped QUADRILATERALS by joining

dots on the 9-dot square.

Two have been drawn already.

There are 16 altogether.

HAPPY NUMBERS

44 is HAPPY because :

$$4 \quad 4$$

$$\underset{(16)}{4^2} + \underset{(16)}{4^2} = 32$$

$$\underset{(9)}{3^2} + \underset{(4)}{2^2} = 13$$

$$\underset{(1)}{1^2} + \underset{(9)}{3^2} = 10$$

$$\underset{(1)}{1^2} + \underset{(0)}{0^2} = \boxed{1}$$

If the chain ends in $\boxed{1}$ then the starting number is **HAPPY !**

Otherwise it is **SAD!**

Is 32 a HAPPY number ?
Is 37 a HAPPY number ?

Find some more HAPPY numbers.
Which numbers are SAD ?

DARTS

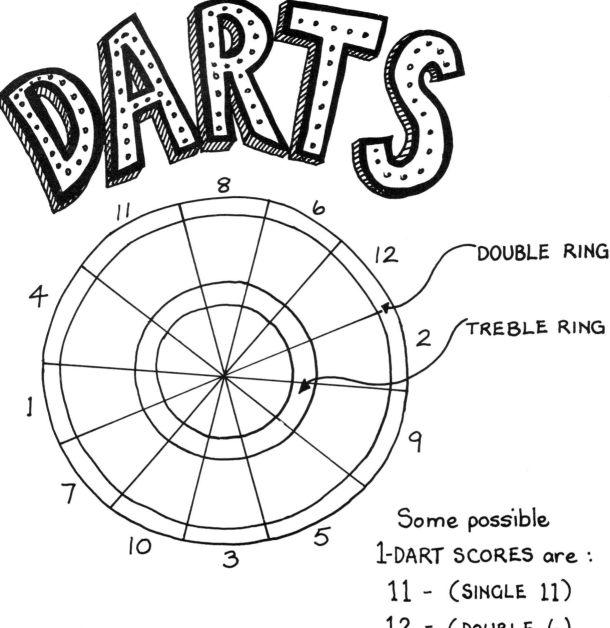

DOUBLE RING

TREBLE RING

8

11

6

12

4

2

1

9

7

5

10

3

Some possible
1-DART SCORES are :
11 - (SINGLE 11)
12 - (DOUBLE 6)
21 - (TREBLE 7)

Some possible 2-DART SCORES are :
13 - (SINGLE 5, SINGLE 8)
25 - (TREBLE 8, SINGLE 1)
21 - (SINGLE 9, DOUBLE 6)

Find ① all possible 1-DART SCORES.
② all possible 2-DART SCORES.
Which scores are not possible?

NAME _____

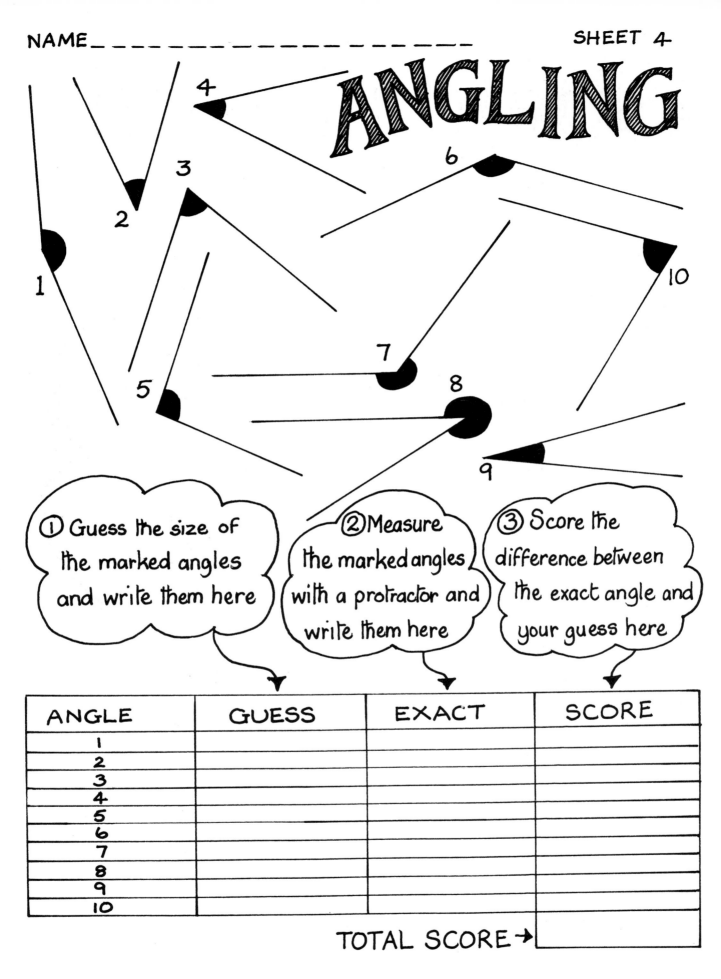

ANGLING

① Guess the size of the marked angles and write them here

② Measure the marked angles with a protractor and write them here

③ Score the difference between the exact angle and your guess here

ANGLE	GUESS	EXACT	SCORE
1			
2			
3			
4			
5			
6			
7			
8			
9			
10			

TOTAL SCORE →

Draw your own angles and play again.

BORED GAME

This is a game for two players, each with a set of counters.

Use two dice : one numbered 1, 2, 4, 5, 6, 7
one numbered 2, 3, 4, 7, 8, 9

RULES Players take turns to throw the dice, multiply the scores together, and, if the answer appears on the board, place a counter on that number.

The first player to place 10 counters wins.

24	8	10	4	56	16	42
18	22	49	40	3	63	35
48	7	45	12	25	20	6
21	15	30	9	14	54	8

The designer of the game has made three mistakes.
Three numbers on the board are impossible. Find them.

Design your own 4×7 board with no mistakes for a game using these dice : one numbered 1, 2, 3, 4, 5, 6
one numbered 3, 4, 5, 7, 8, 9

FOUR DIGITS

Use the digits 1, 2, 5 and 6 and any mathematical signs to make expressions. A digit may only be used once in each expression.

Here are some examples:

$8 = 5 + 2 + 1$

$12 = 2 \times 6$

$14 = 16 - 2$

Try to find expressions for the numbers 1 to 30

No.	Expression	No.	Expression
1		16	
2		17	
3		18	
4		19	
5		20	
6		21	
7		22	
8		23	
9		24	
10		25	
11		26	
12		27	
13		28	
14		29	
15		30	

Now try with the digits 1, 2, 4 and 9

Put the digits 1, 1, 2, 3, 3, 4, 5, 6 in the boxes to make four two-digit numbers.

Add the four numbers together.

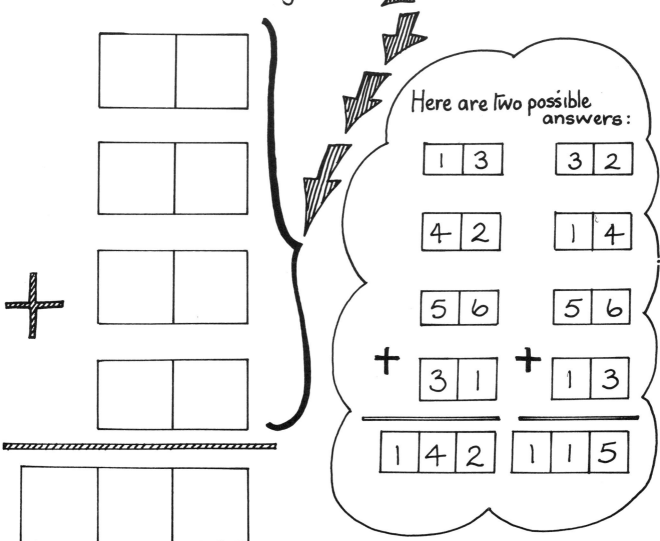

There are 12 different possible answers.

Can you find them?

Now try with 1, 2, 2, 3, 4, 4, 5, 5

Shapely

Draw a square 8 cm × 8 cm on card.

Mark these mid-points and draw these lines.

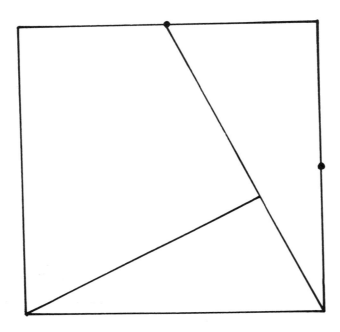

Cut out the three pieces.

Join the pieces edge-to-edge to make the following shapes:

       TRIANGLE

       SQUARE

       RECTANGLE

       PARALLELOGRAM

       TRAPEZIUM

       PENTAGON

       HEXAGON

Can you make any other shapes?

A MATHEMATICS TRIVIAL PURSUITS has these categories :

(AP)   ANGLES AND POLYGONS

(A)   ARITHMETIC

(N)   NUMBERS

(PL)   POT LUCK

(M)   MEASUREMENT

(S)   SHAPE

Here is a card, with the answers on the back.

(AP) What is the name of a five-sided polygon?

(A) What is 14 × 20 ?

(N) What is the nearest prime number to 20 ?

(PL) What date within the last hundred years reads the same upside down ?

(M) How many centimetres in 1 metre?

(S) How many edges has a cube?

FRONT

(AP) PENTAGON

(A) 280

(N) 19

(PL) 1961

(M) 100

(S) 12

BACK

Make four more cards.

Test them out on your friends.

Invent your own headings and make a card.

Castles

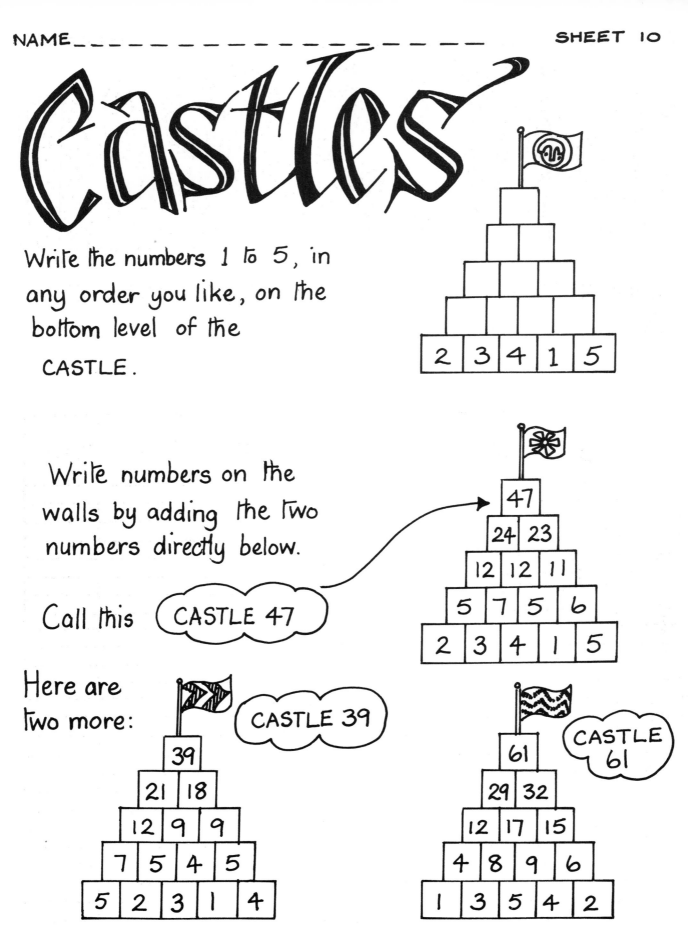

Write the numbers 1 to 5, in any order you like, on the bottom level of the CASTLE.

2 3 4 1 5

Write numbers on the walls by adding the two numbers directly below.

Call this CASTLE 47

47
24 23
12 12 11
5 7 5 6
2 3 4 1 5

Here are two more:

CASTLE 39

39
21 18
12 9 9
7 5 4 5
5 2 3 1 4

CASTLE 61

61
29 32
12 17 15
4 8 9 6
1 3 5 4 2

One of the CASTLES 50 to 59 is impossible. Which one?

Complete the table by writing down the DIVISORS of the numbers 1 to 50.

	DIVISORS	Total		DIVISORS	Total
1	1	1	26		
2	1, 2	2	27		
3	1, 3	2	28		
4	1, 2, 4	3	29		
5	1, 5	2	30		
6	1, 2, 3, 6	4	31		
7			32		
8			33		
9			34		
10	1, 2, 5, 10	4	35		
11			36		
12			37		
13			38		
14			39		
15			40		
16			41		
17			42		
18			43		
19			44		
20			45		
21			46		
22			47		
23			48		
24			49		
25			50		

Try to describe the numbers which have 2 DIVISORS,

3 DIVISORS, _ _ _ _ _ _

Draw differently shaped TRIANGLES by joining dots in these 12-DOT rectangles. Two have been drawn already. There are 20 altogether.

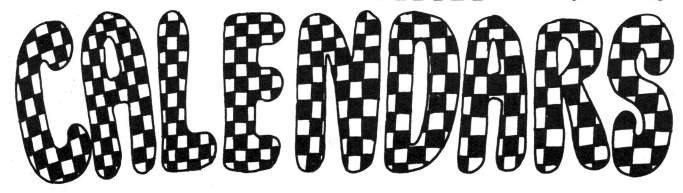

CALENDARS

MAY

SUN	MON	TUES	WED	THUR	FRI	SAT
				1	2	3
4	5	6	7	8	9	10
11	12	13	14	15	16	17
18	19	20	21	22	23	24
25	26	27	28	29	30	31

Take a 3 × 3 square of numbers from the calendar.

6	7	8
13	14	15
20	21	22

$\bigcirc \times \bigcirc =$

$\diamond \times \diamond =$ _____

DIFFERENCE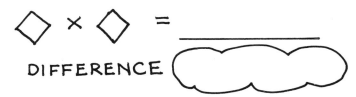

Take some other 3 × 3 squares from the calendar.
What do you notice?
Repeat with this month's calendar.

DAVID'S HOMEWORK

Mark DAVID'S HOMEWORK. Award 1 MARK for every correct sum, and draw a circle round the errors in the others.

①
```
    35
  ×42
  1400
    70
  1470
```

②
```
    28
  ×46
  1120
   168
  1288
```

③
```
    16
  × 43
   640
    64
   704
```

④
```
    54
  × 38
  1620
   452
  2072
```

⑤
```
    36
  × 27
   720
   252
   972
```

⑥
```
    72
  ×51
  3600
    72
  3672
```

⑦
```
    73
  × 44
  2920
   292
  3212
```

⑧
```
    67
  × 29
  1340
   613
  1953
```

⑨
```
    82
  × 19
   820
   638
  1458
```

⑩
```
    49
  × 37
  1470
   343
  1813
```

Make four errors in these ten sums and ask your friend to mark your work.

① 46 × 27 ② 17 × 19 ③ 48 × 63 ④ 21 × 41 ⑤ 92 × 23

⑥ 37 × 28 ⑦ 43 × 19 ⑧ 28 × 29 ⑨ 86 × 31 ⑩ 75 × 48

Put one of the SIGNS $(+, \times, -)$ in every gap, and use BRACKETS to make balanced equations.

EXAMPLE : $(5 + 3) \times 2 = 16$

① 9___3___2 = 24

② 5___4___6 = 50

③ 7___5___2 = 21

④ 8___5___4 = 12

⑤ 6___3___7 = 63

⑥ 5___4___6___1 = 45

⑦ 5___6___2___3 = 14

⑧ 7___5___4___3 = 24

⑨ 9___3___6___5 = 36

⑩ 8___2___5___1 = 24

Invent ten equations with gaps, and test your work out on a friend.

Make an answer sheet first.

Sunshine and Rain

This data relates to 19th August 1988

ENGLAND	sunshine (hours)	rain (inches)	SCOTLAND	sunshine (hours)	rain (inches)
BIRMINGHAM	8·5	0·10	ABERDEEN	1·0	0·09
BRISTOL	7·8	0·15	AVIEMORE	0·6	0·09
BUXTON	6·8	0·29	DUNBAR	–	0·44
CARLISLE	4·5	0·16	EDINBURGH	–	0·54
LEEDS	5·0	0·07	ESKDALEMUIR	1·8	0·62
LONDON	5·1	0·33	GLASGOW	3·6	0·21
MANCHESTER	5·2	0·27	KINLOSS	1·4	0·18
NEWCASTLE	2·1	0·12	LERWICK	5·0	0·81
NORWICH	7·8	0·08	LEUCHARS	–	0·32
NOTTINGHAM	4·4	0·18	PRESTWICK	4·4	0·14
PLYMOUTH	8·6	0·09	STORNOWAY	–	0·15
ROSS-ON-WYE	11·4	0·02	TIREE	4·1	0·19
			WICK	2·9	0·27

Ⓐ Find pairs of towns with SUNSHINE HOURS differing by

a) 2 HOURS

b) 1 HOUR

c) 1½ HOURS

d) 3½ HOURS

e) 2·3 HOURS

Ⓑ Find pairs of towns with RAINFALL differing by

a) 0·3 INCHES

b) 0·2 INCHES

c) 0·15 INCHES

d) 0·05 INCHES

e) 0·08 INCHES

Ⓒ Choose any 10 towns and draw separate bar charts to show

a) SUNSHINE HOURS, and b) RAINFALL

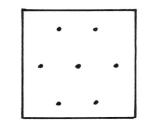

Draw differently shaped polygons by joining the dots on this hexagonal board.

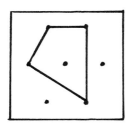 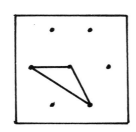

Here are two.

There are seventeen more.

Can you find them ?

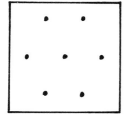 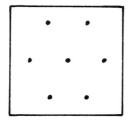 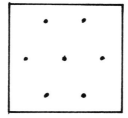 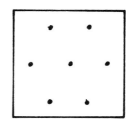 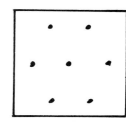

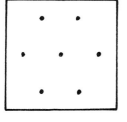 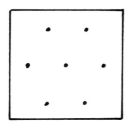 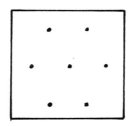 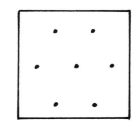 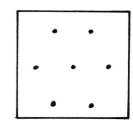

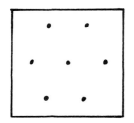 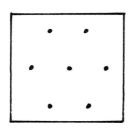 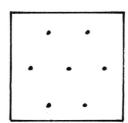 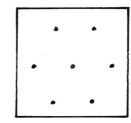 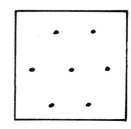

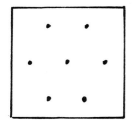 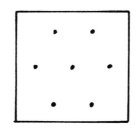

MASTERMIND

You are entering a MATHEMATICS MASTERMIND COMPETITION.

Your specialist subject is "ANGLES". Here are the first ten questions.

1. Name an instrument for measuring the angle between two straight lines.

2. What is the angle between perpendicular lines?

3. What name is given to an angle less than 90°?

4. What 3-figure bearing represents the direction S.W.?

5. What are the angles of a set-square?

6. What is the size of any angle in an equilateral triangle?

7. Two angles of a triangle are 47° and 74°. What is the other?

8. How many degrees in half a right-angle?

9. Through what angle does the minute hand of a clock move in 1 minute?

10. If an isosceles triangle has an angle of 110°, what is the size of the other angles?

How many can you score out of 10?

Invent ten questions for a different specialist subject.
eg. "SHAPE", "DECIMALS", "THE CIRCLE", "TIME".

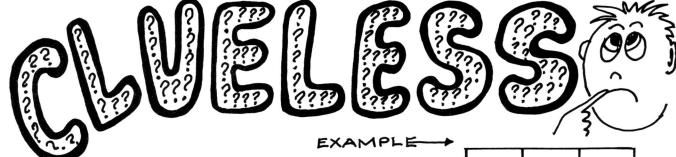

CLUELESS

EXAMPLE →

Write the numbers 1 to 9
in the boxes of each puzzle to
match the row and column totals.

Some clues are given :

7	3	4	14
1	5	9	15
6	8	2	16
14	16	15	

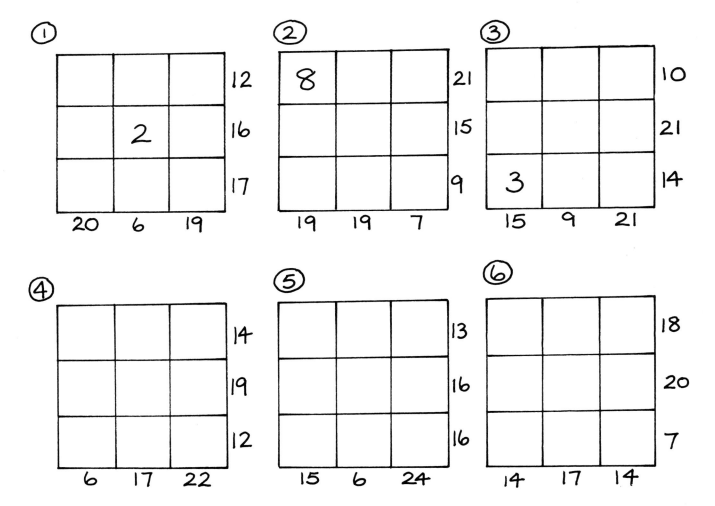

①
			12
	2		16
			17
20	6	19	

②
8			21
			15
			9
19	19	7	

③
			10
			21
	3		14
15	9	21	

④
			14
			19
			12
6	17	22	

⑤
			13
			16
			16
15	6	24	

⑥
			18
			20
			7
14	17	14	

Try them on scrap paper first.
Invent some similar puzzles using numbers 6 to 14.

Try this puzzle

1. THINK OF A NUMBER
2. ADD 2
3. THEN MULTIPLY BY 3
4. THEN TAKE AWAY 6
5. THEN TAKE AWAY THE NUMBER
   YOU FIRST THOUGHT OF.
6. HALVE IT

X

$X + 2$

$3X + 6$

$3X$

$2X$

X

Here's another

1. THINK OF A NUMBER
2. ADD 4
3. DOUBLE IT
4. ADD THE NUMBER YOU
   FIRST THOUGHT OF.
5. TAKE AWAY 8.
6. DIVIDE BY 3

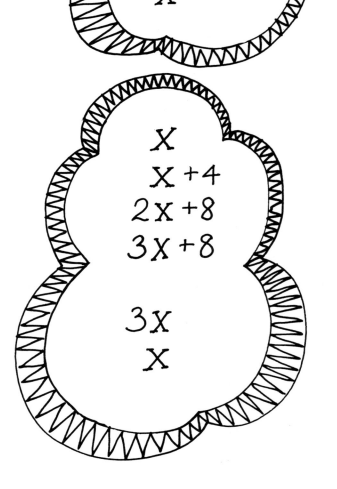

X
$X + 4$
$2X + 8$
$3X + 8$

$3X$
X

Invent some of your own.
Try them out on friends.

RECTANGLES

1	2	3	4	5	6	7	8	9	10
11	12	13	14	15	16	17	18	19	20
21	22	23	24	25	26	27	28	29	30
31	32	33	34	35	36	37	38	39	40
41	42	43	44	45	46	47	48	49	50
51	52	53	54	55	56	57	58	59	60
61	62	63	64	65	66	67	68	69	70
71	72	73	74	75	76	77	78	79	80
81	82	83	84	85	86	87	88	89	90
91	92	93	94	95	96	97	98	99	100

Here are two RECTANGLES in the square.

6	7	8	9
16	17	18	19
26	27	28	29

2	3
12	13
22	23
32	33

6 + 29 = 35   2 + 33 = 35

9 + 26 = 35   3 + 32 = 35

The opposite corners sum to 35.

Find five more RECTANGLES or SQUARES whose opposite corners sum to 35.

How many can you find whose opposite corners sum to 50 ?

Change the 50 to another number and repeat for other sums, eg. 120

Place 3 black and 3 white counters
on the board like this :

A counter moves by sliding it
one space, horizontally or vertically
into an empty box.

The object is to swap the positions of
the black and white counters.
Can you do it in 16 moves?
Record the moves.
Now try this.

Invent a similar puzzle of your own.
How many moves are required?

The Great Divide

Place the digits 1,2,3,3,4,5,5,6,6 in the boxes for each puzzle.
Place them, where possible, so that they DIVIDE into
the ROW HEADING and the COLUMN HEADING.
Each digit which divides into it's ROW HEADING scores
1 point, and also if it divides into its COLUMN HEADING.

EXAMPLE

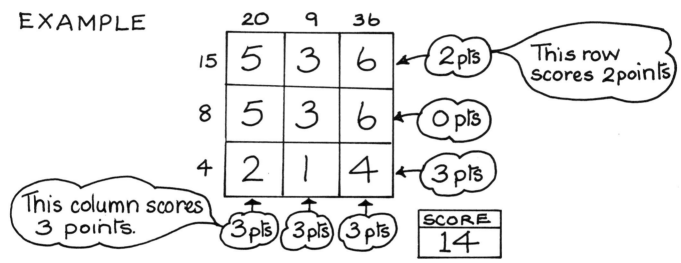

Score as many points as you can with these:
Try them on scrap paper first.

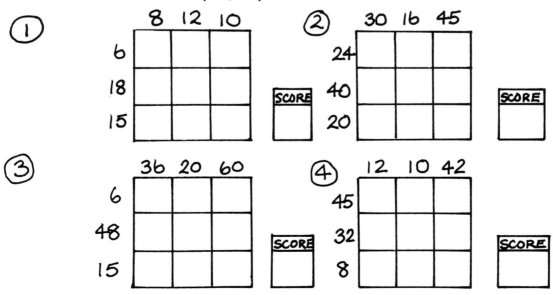

Now try each puzzle with 1,2,2,3,4,4,4,5,6.

Signposts

You are given a TARGET ③
and a set of numbers $\boxed{3, 4, 5, 6, 8}$

SCORE 1 PT. for each use of an ADDITION SIGN.
　　　　2 PTS. for each use of a SUBTRACTION SIGN.
　　　　3 PTS. for each use of a MULTIPLICATION SIGN.
　　　　4 PTS. for each use of a DIVISION SIGN.

So ③ $= 8 + 5 - 6 - 4$　　SCORES 5 PTS.
　 ③ $= (6 \times 4) \div 8$　　SCORES 7 PTS.
　 ③ $= 64 - 53 - 8$　　SCORES 4 PTS.

How many points can you score with these ?

	SET OF NUMBERS	TARGET	EXPRESSION	SCORE
1.	3, 4, 5, 6, 8	4		
2.	5, 6, 7, 1, 2	5		
3.	3, 8, 5, 9, 2	3		
4.	2, 3, 4, 6, 7	8		
5.	4, 5, 3, 2, 6	7		
6.	1, 3, 5, 7, 9	2		
7.	2, 4, 6, 8, 3	9		
8.	4, 6, 8, 5, 9	20		
			TOTAL	

Make expressions by ADDING CONSECUTIVE WHOLE NUMBERS.

EXAMPLES : ⑨ = 4 + 5

⑭ = 2 + 3 + 4 + 5

⑱ = 5 + 6 + 7

Try to find expressions by ADDING CONSECUTIVE WHOLE NUMBERS for the numbers ① to ㊵

①		㉑	
②		㉒	
③		㉓	
④		㉔	
⑤		㉕	
⑥		㉖	
⑦		㉗	
⑧		㉘	
⑨		㉙	
⑩		㉚	
⑪		㉛	
⑫		㉜	
⑬		㉝	
⑭		㉞	
⑮		㉟	
⑯		㊱	
⑰		㊲	
⑱		㊳	
⑲		㊴	
⑳		㊵	

☛ You may photocopy this page for use in the classroom ☚

The table shows temperatures around the world on 20th August 1988

Lunch-time reports

		C	F			C	F
Ajaccio	S	29	84	London	C	20	68
Algiers	S	33	91	*L. Angeles	C	20	68
Amsterdam	F	20	68	Luxembourg	R	21	70
Athens	S	32	90	Madrid	S	33	91
Bahrain	S	37	99	Majorca	F	30	86
Barcelona	F	29	84	Malaga	C	28	82
Belgrade	S	29	84	Malta	F	29	84
Berlin	S	28	82	Melbourne	F	16	61
*Bermuda	R	30	86	*Mexico City	C	18	64
Biarritz	F	25	77	*Miami	S	31	88
Birmingham	F	18	64	*Montreal	F	19	66
*B. Aires	S	22	72	Moscow	C	14	57
Bombay	F	26	79	Munich	S	30	86
Bordeaux	C	21	70	Nairobi	C	21	70
*Boston	C	23	73	Naples	S	32	90
Bristol	R	16	61	*Nassau	F	32	90
Brussels	F	21	70	Newcastle	R	13	55
Budapest	S	27	81	New Dehli	C	29	84
Cairo	S	34	93	*New York	S	27	81
Cape Town	S	19	66	Nice	S	29	84
Cardiff	F	18	64	Oporto	S	23	73
Casblanca	S	29	84	Oslo	R	14	57
*Chicago	F	29	84	Paris	F	23	73
Cologne	R	20	68	Peking	C	28	82
Copenhagen	C	19	66	Perth	F	17	63
Corfu	S	33	91	Prague	S	27	81
*Dallas	F	34	93	Reykjavik	S	14	57
*Denver	S	23	73	Rhodes	S	32	90
Dublin	C	17	63	*Rio de Jan.	S	23	73
Dubrovnik	S	29	84	Riyadh	S	43	109
Edinburgh	R	14	57	Rome	S	30	86
Faro	S	29	84	Salzburg	S	29	84
Florence	S	34	93	Seoul	F	30	86
Frankfurt	F	28	82	Singapore	R	26	79
Funchal	S	26	79	Stockholm	R	16	61
Geneva	S	31	88	Strasbourg	F	29	84
Gibraltar	S	26	79	Sydney	S	22	72
Glasgow	C	14	57	Tangier	S	31	88
Helsinki	C	15	59	Tel Aviv	S	30	86
Hong Kong	C	28	82	Tenerife	S	28	82
Innsbruck	S	29	84	Tokyo	F	29	84
Inverness	C	14	57	Tunis	F	32	90
Istanbul	S	29	84	Valencia	S	32	90
Jersey	F	17	63	*Vancouver	F	17	63
Jo'burg	S	15	59	Venice	S	28	82
Karachi	C	32	90	Vienna	S	28	82
Larnaca	S	31	88	Warsaw	S	23	73
Las Palmas	S	24	75	*Washington	F	31	88
Lisbon	S	27	81	Wellington	S	8	46
Locarno	C	22	72	Zurich	S	29	84

C cloudy, Dr drizzle, F fair, Fg fog, H hail, R rain,
Sl sleet, Sn snow, S sunny, Th thunder.
* Previous day's readings

TEMP IN °F

(bar chart with bars for CHICAGO and OSLO, scale 50–90)

Choose 10 places.

Draw a bar chart to show their temperatures in °F. Use today's newspaper to draw another chart for the same 10 places. Compare.

Complete as much of the table as possible.

Each expression uses up to three of the digits at the top of the column.

Digits may not be repeated in an expression.

Expressions may not be repeated in a column.

	2,3,8	5,1,4	3,6,4
ODD NUMBER			
EVEN NUMBER			
PRIME NUMBER BETWEEN 10 AND 40	23		43 − 6
PRIME NUMBER BETWEEN 50 AND 100			
SQUARE NUMBER			
CUBE NUMBER			
DIVISOR OF 36	8 − 2		
TRIANGULAR NUMBER			
NUMBER LESS THAN 12			
NUMBER MORE THAN 60		51 × 4	
NUMBER BETWEEN 10 AND 20			
MULTIPLE OF 3			
MULTIPLE OF 4			
MULTIPLE OF 5			36 + 4

Middlin'

Use the digits 2, 3, 4, 5, 7, 9 to make three two-digit numbers.

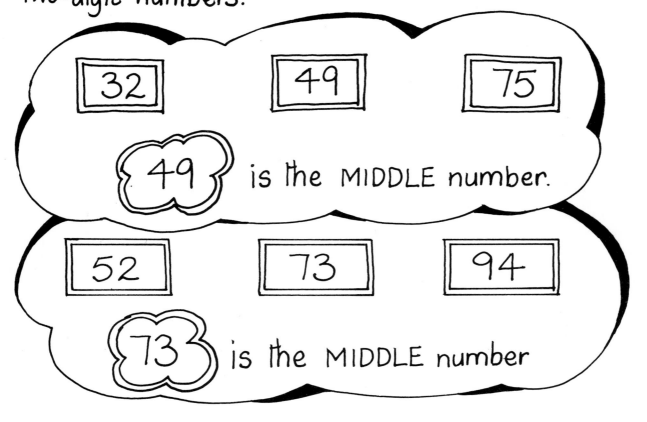

32   49   75

49 is the MIDDLE number.

52   73   94

73 is the MIDDLE number

How many different MIDDLE numbers are possible?

Now try with the digits 3, 3, 4, 5, 5, 8

Place + and − signs inside the circles to make the equations BALANCE.

EXAMPLE   7 ⊕ 5 ⊖ 3 = 9

①   4 ◯ 9 ◯ 3 = 16
②   5 ◯ 8 ◯ 3 = 10
③   6 ◯ 2 ◯ 1 = 3
④   9 ◯ 6 ◯ 8 = 11
⑤   6 ◯ 1 ◯ 4 = 9

⑥   6 ◯ 7 ◯ 8 ◯ 2 = 19
⑦   5 ◯ 4 ◯ 3 ◯ 1 = 7
⑧   6 ◯ 3 ◯ 5 ◯ 2 = 0
⑨   4 ◯ 4 ◯ 6 ◯ 1 = 7
⑩   9 ◯ 3 ◯ 7 ◯ 1 = 4

Invent ten of these of your own.

Try them out on a friend.

Travel round the board making moves like a CHESS KNIGHT. Try to land on each square once and only once.
The starting positions are given.

Knighty Knight

EXAMPLE

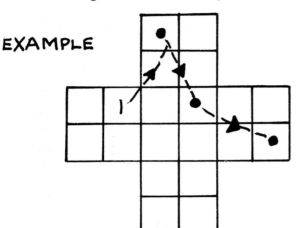

	2	15		
	13	10		
12	1	16	3	14	9
17	6	11	8	19	4
	18	5		
	7	20		

Now try these :

 ①

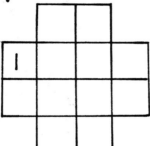

②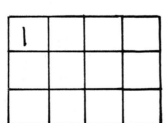

 ③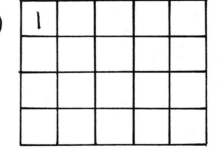

④

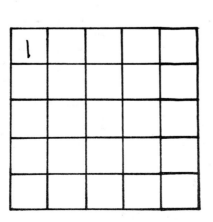

⑤

MISPRINTS

TWIDDINGTON'S CARD GAME COMPANY have produced a card game.
Players have to collect sets of four cards of equivalent fractions.

Here is one set ⟶ $\dfrac{1}{3}$ $\dfrac{2}{6}$ $\dfrac{3}{9}$ $\dfrac{4}{12}$

The rest of the cards have been jumbled up.
Two cards have MISPRINTS.   Which ones ?

$\dfrac{4}{6}$ $\dfrac{3}{18}$ $\dfrac{12}{15}$ $\dfrac{3}{6}$ $\dfrac{1}{6}$ $\dfrac{6}{16}$

$\dfrac{20}{24}$ $\dfrac{6}{8}$ $\dfrac{1}{2}$ $\dfrac{12}{20}$ $\dfrac{2}{10}$ $\dfrac{4}{32}$ $\dfrac{5}{6}$

$\dfrac{4}{16}$ $\dfrac{10}{12}$ $\dfrac{2}{8}$ $\dfrac{24}{3}$ $\dfrac{3}{5}$ $\dfrac{3}{4}$ $\dfrac{5}{6}$

$\dfrac{1}{5}$ $\dfrac{4}{24}$ $\dfrac{9}{0}$ $\dfrac{8}{12}$ $\dfrac{2}{3}$ $\dfrac{16}{20}$ $\dfrac{1}{8}$

$\dfrac{4}{5}$ $\dfrac{9}{12}$ $\dfrac{10}{8}$ $\dfrac{3}{12}$ $\dfrac{3}{15}$ $\dfrac{5}{6}$

$\dfrac{15}{18}$ $\dfrac{4}{8}$ $\dfrac{8}{20}$ $\dfrac{20}{4}$ $\dfrac{2}{16}$ $\dfrac{2}{12}$ $\dfrac{9}{6}$

Invent your own MISPRINT puzzle.

EXCEPTIONS

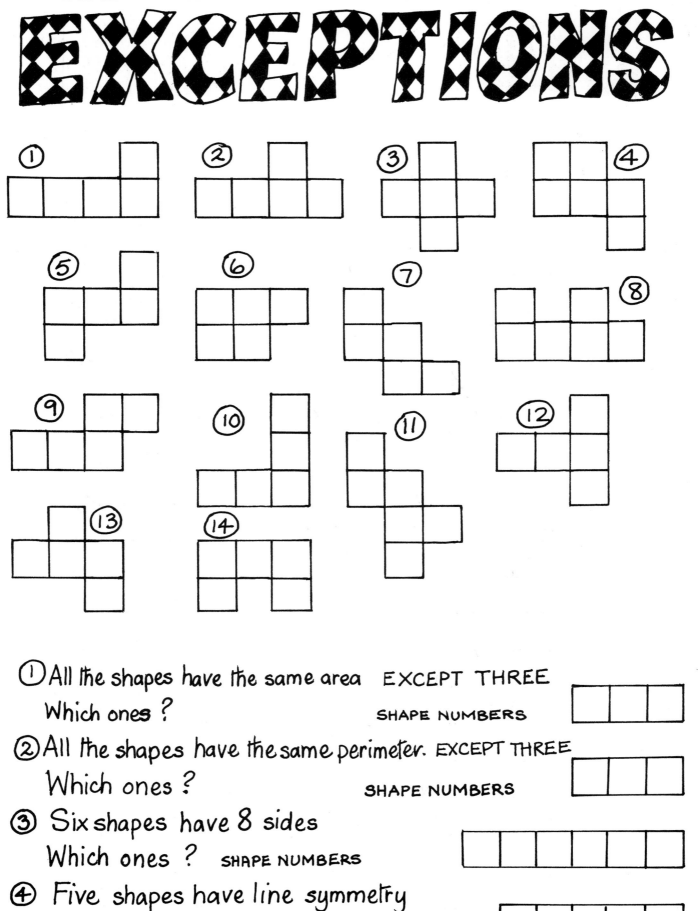

① All the shapes have the same area EXCEPT THREE
Which ones ?   SHAPE NUMBERS

② All the shapes have the same perimeter. EXCEPT THREE
Which ones ?   SHAPE NUMBERS

③ Six shapes have 8 sides
Which ones ?   SHAPE NUMBERS

④ Five shapes have line symmetry
Which ones?   SHAPE NUMBERS

Numbers in the left square are multiplied to make the numbers in the right square.

2	8	3	ROW TOTAL 13
7	4	6	17
5	1	9	15

×4 =

8	32	12	ROW TOTAL 52
28	16	24	68
20	4	36	60

①

2		3	ROW TOTAL —
	7		—
9		1	—

×4 =

	20		ROW TOTAL —
24		32	—
	16		—

②

4	3		ROW TOTAL 13
9		1	12
	5	7	20

×5 =

			ROW TOTAL —
			—
			—

③

3		7	ROW TOTAL —
2	6		—
	4	1	—

×3 =

			ROW TOTAL 57
			48
			30

④

			ROW TOTAL 16
			17
			12

×6 =

48		12	ROW TOTAL —
	42	6	—
30		18	—

Invent four more puzzles like this and make a note of the answers.

PHASES

Try to solve these twenty-five anagrams.

They are all mathematical shapes.

When you have solved the anagram, draw the shape.

	ANAGRAM	SHAPE
1	RECLIC	
2	ONCE	
3	GOATNOC	
4	DIMPRAY	
5	CANDORHODDEE	
6	QUEARS	
7	SMIRP	
8	NIGLERAT	
9	SHODICONARE	
10	NAPGOTEN	
11	REPESH	
12	GALLOPMARRELA	
13	ROTTENHEARD	
14	CONDAGE	
15	BUEC	
16	LECTGRANE	
17	ROLYPHONED	
18	TIKE	
19	CHAREOTOND	
20	SHURBOM	
21	DRINCLEY	
22	AQUATIDELLARR	
23	BODICU	
24	NAXEHOG	
25	REATIZUMP	

Invent 10 anagrams for mathematical words.

eg. fractions, ratio,_____   Try them out on a friend.

CROSSPATCH

Mark CROSSES on the boards.
Each ROW, COLUMN and DIAGONAL must not contain more than ONE CROSS.

EXAMPLE

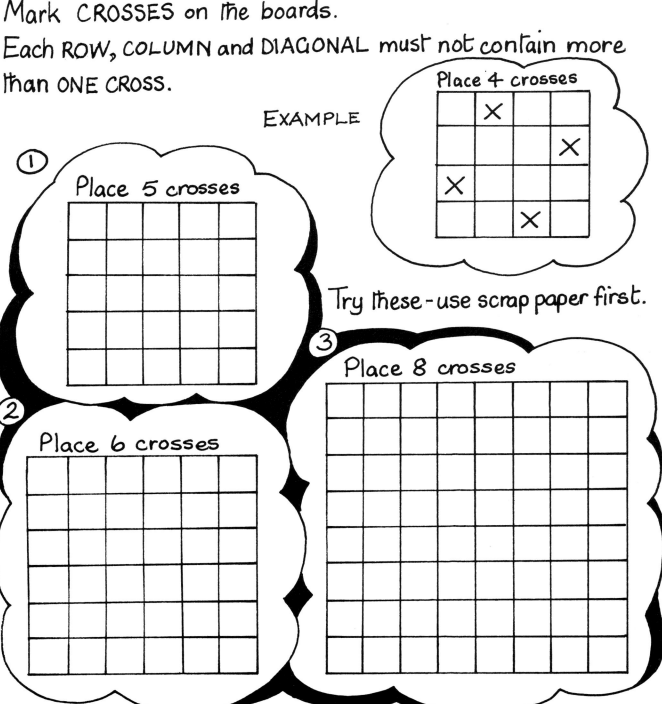

Place 4 crosses

① Place 5 crosses

Try these - use scrap paper first.

③ Place 8 crosses

② Place 6 crosses

Now try to place 12 crosses on board number ② so that every ROW, COLUMN and DIAGONAL does not contain more than two CROSSES.

BILLS

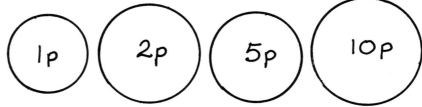

You have 4 coins only.

A 3p BILL can be paid using the 1p coin and the 2p coin.

1p, 2p

An 8p BILL can be paid using the 5p coin, the 2p coin and the 1p coin.

5p, 2p, 1p

How could you pay these bills? Two are impossible.

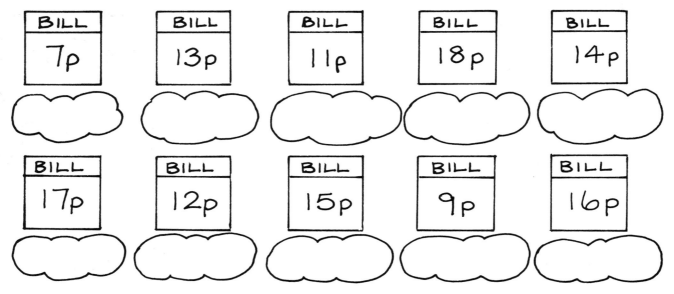

What bills could you pay with these 4 coins?

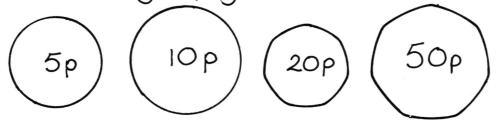

BIG AITCH

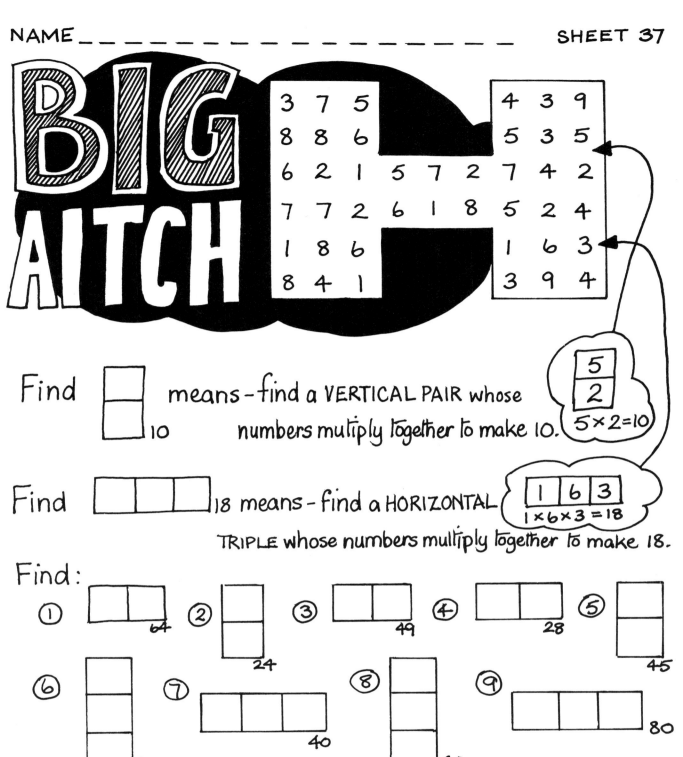

Find ▯ (vertical pair box) 10 means – find a VERTICAL PAIR whose numbers multiply together to make 10.

$5 \times 2 = 10$

Find ▭▭▭ 18 means – find a HORIZONTAL TRIPLE whose numbers multiply together to make 18.

$1 \times 6 \times 3 = 18$

Find:

① 64

② 24

③ 49

④ 28

⑤ 45

⑥ 36

⑦ 40

⑧ 40

⑨ 80

⑩ 75

⑪ 90

⑫ 140

⑬ 175

Devise your own set of questions.

FIND FIVE

Use 1, 2, 4, 5 and 8 only.

Here are FIVE different expressions for

$$26 \quad = \quad 25 + 1$$
$$= \quad 28 + 4 - 5 - 1$$
$$= \quad 18 + (2 \times 4)$$
$$= \quad 54 - 28$$
$$= \quad 2 \times (18 - 5)$$

Find FIVE different expressions for these numbers.

	32	23	16
1.			
2.			
3.			
4.			
5.			

Choose your own three numbers and try to find FIVE
different expressions for them using the digits
1, 2, 4, 5, 8.

NAME _ SHEET 39

SHADASHAPE

EXAMPLE:
These are
MID-POINTS.

ISOSCELES TRIANGLE

Shade regions to make the named shapes.
All the shapes must be different.

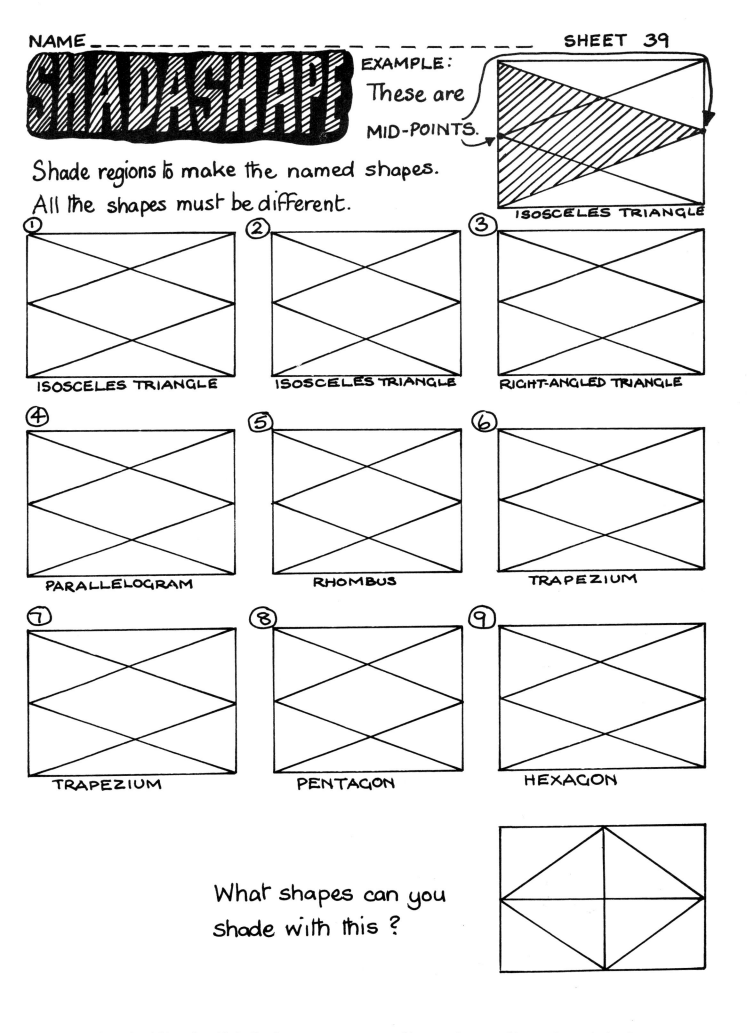

① ISOSCELES TRIANGLE

② ISOSCELES TRIANGLE

③ RIGHT-ANGLED TRIANGLE

④ PARALLELOGRAM

⑤ RHOMBUS

⑥ TRAPEZIUM

⑦ TRAPEZIUM

⑧ PENTAGON

⑨ HEXAGON

What shapes can you
shade with this?

TENSION

Make shapes by joining five squares edge
to edge.   Here are two : ⟶

There are 10 more.   Can you find them ?

Draw them on the squared paper.

Subnormal

Put the digits 1, 3, 5 and 6 in these boxes to make two two-digit numbers. Do the subtraction sum.

Here are two possible answers:—

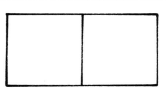

There are 12 different possible answers. Can you find them?

NOTE: The top number must be larger than the bottom number.

Now try with: 2, 5, 7 and 8

HAT TRICKS

Draw 2 numbers from a HAT.
The TRICK is to make two-digit PRIME NUMBERS.

[5] [3] This HAT-TRICK can be done in 7 ways.

1 3	1 9	3 1	4 1

4 3	5 3	5 9

Solve these HAT-TRICKS.

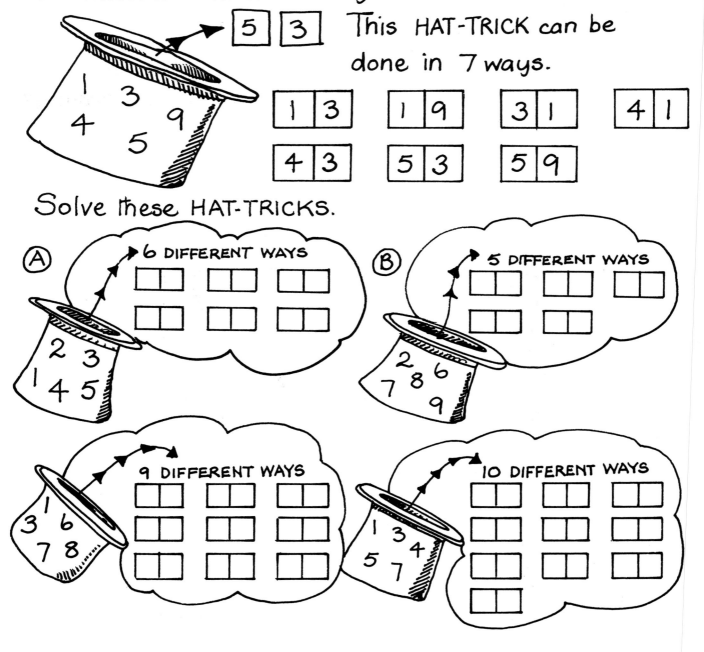

Ⓐ 6 DIFFERENT WAYS

Ⓑ 5 DIFFERENT WAYS

9 DIFFERENT WAYS

10 DIFFERENT WAYS

Which five numbers enable the HAT-TRICK to be done in twelve different ways?

Satisfaction

Write the numbers 1 to 16, one in each box, so that all numbers satisfy __both__ row headings and column headings.

Try it on scrap paper first.

	EVEN NUMBERS	MULTIPLES OF 2	ODD NUMBERS	PRIME NUMBERS
NUMBERS BETWEEN 11 AND 18				
NUMBERS LESS THAN 12				
FACTORS OF 36				
NUMBERS LESS THAN 7				

Design a square with categories of your own and ask a friend to solve it.

Side-Splitters

Draw polygons with different numbers of sides.
Two have been done already.

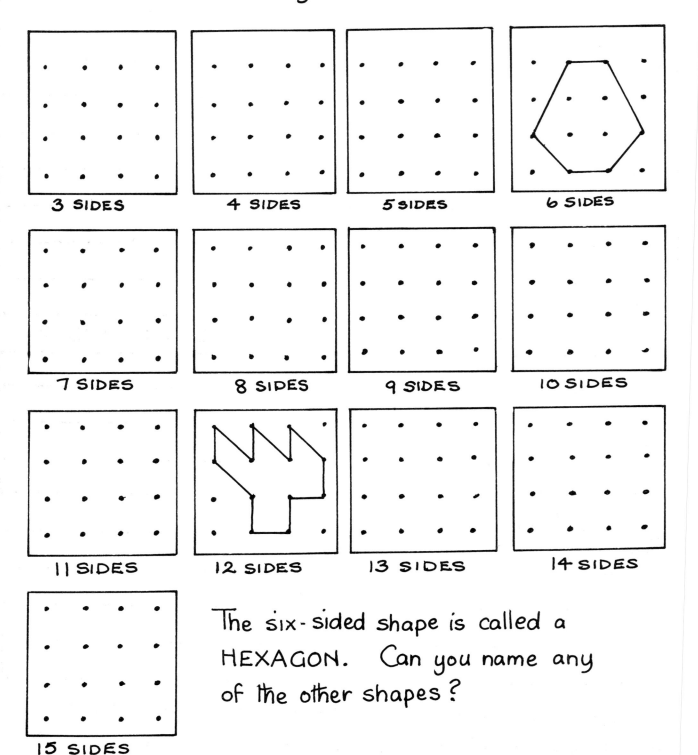

The six-sided shape is called a
HEXAGON. Can you name any
of the other shapes?

Entries must begin with the letter on the left.
How many can you find?

	UNITS OF MEASUREMENT	SHAPES
A		
C		
D		
E		
F		
G		
H		
I	INCH	ISOSCELES TRIANGLE
K		
L		
N		NONAGON
O		
P	PINT	
Q		
R		
S		
T		

Can you find any entries for different starting letters eg. M?
Invent your own title and see how many entries you can find.

FILL-INS

$1 \rightarrow 3 \rightarrow 4 \rightarrow 7 \rightarrow 11 \rightarrow 18$

$3 \rightarrow 7 \rightarrow 10 \rightarrow 17 \rightarrow 27 \rightarrow 44$

Try to discover how these chains of numbers are made.
See if you can fill in the gaps.

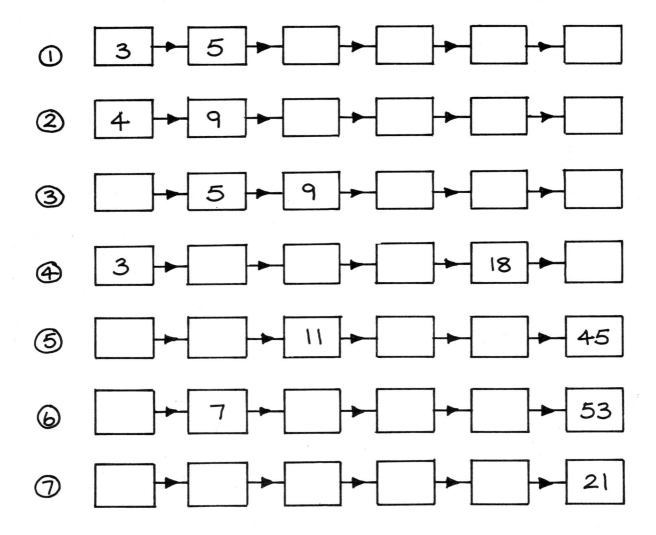

① $3 \rightarrow 5 \rightarrow \square \rightarrow \square \rightarrow \square \rightarrow \square$

② $4 \rightarrow 9 \rightarrow \square \rightarrow \square \rightarrow \square \rightarrow \square$

③ $\square \rightarrow 5 \rightarrow 9 \rightarrow \square \rightarrow \square \rightarrow \square$

④ $3 \rightarrow \square \rightarrow \square \rightarrow \square \rightarrow 18 \rightarrow \square$

⑤ $\square \rightarrow \square \rightarrow 11 \rightarrow \square \rightarrow \square \rightarrow 45$

⑥ $\square \rightarrow 7 \rightarrow \square \rightarrow \square \rightarrow \square \rightarrow 53$

⑦ $\square \rightarrow \square \rightarrow \square \rightarrow \square \rightarrow \square \rightarrow 21$

Make up some of your own puzzles like this.

3	7	2	9	1
4	6	3	8	6
1	8	4	5	3
5	1	2	7	6
5	9	7	4	2

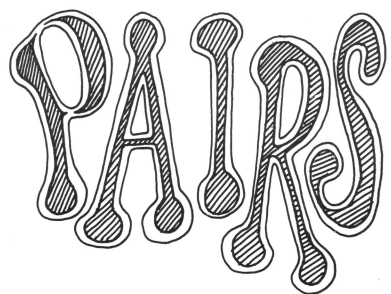

Look at horizontal and vertical PAIRS.

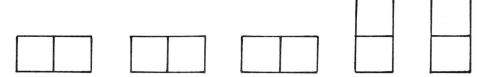

There are nine different PAIRS with a total of 9. Can you find them?

Find five different PAIRS with a total of 10.

All PAIR TOTALS can be found between 3 and 17 except two.
Which ones ?
Create your own square and make up some questions like these.

CORNER NUMBERS

Use numbers 1 to 10 only.

Each number can only be used once in each picture.

The corner numbers must add up to the numbers inside the shape.

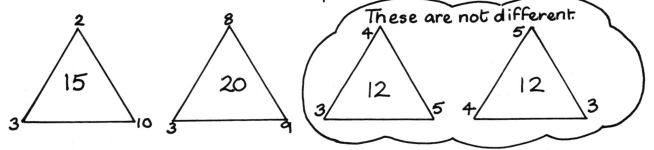

2 / 15 \ 3 ... 10   8 / 20 \ 3 ... 9

These are not different.

4 / 12 \ 3 ... 5   5 / 12 \ 4 ... 3

Ⓐ Find seven different triangles. Write the numbers in the corners.

12   12   12   12   12   12   12

Ⓑ Find ten different triangles.

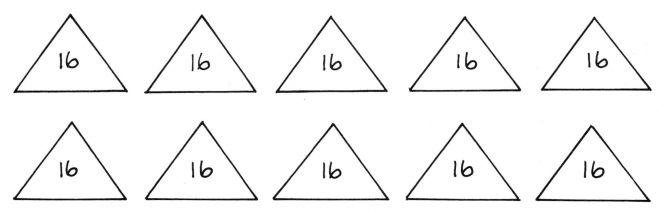

16   16   16   16   16

16   16   16   16   16

Ⓒ Find six different squares.

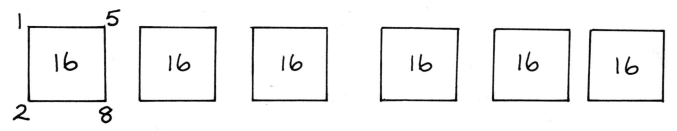

1 ⌐ 5 / 16 / 2 ⌐ 8   16   16   16   16   16

SYMMETRY

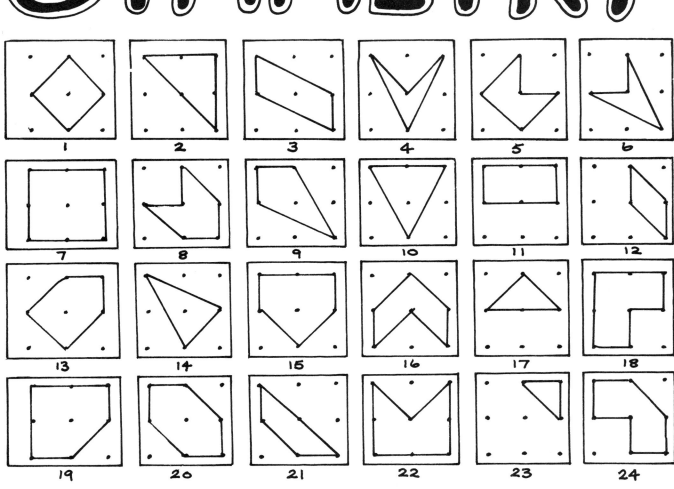

Two of these shapes have no lines of symmetry.
Which ones ?

Draw the lines of symmetry on the other shapes.

Which shapes have more than one line of symmetry?

Which shapes have rotational symmetry ?

Draw your own symmetrical
shapes on this sized grid.

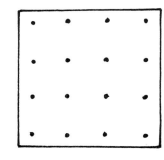

QUADS

The sixteen quadrilaterals are:

HAPPY NUMBERS

A chain produces a collection of HAPPY numbers.

For example:
$$94$$
$$81 + 16 = 97$$
$$81 + 49 = 130$$
$$1 + 9 + 0 = 10$$
$$1 + 0 = \boxed{1}$$

So 94, 97, 130, 10 are HAPPY

Obviously if 97 is HAPPY, so is 79.

$$37 \longleftarrow$$
$$9 + 49 = 58$$
$$25 + 64 = 89$$
$$64 + 81 = 145$$
$$1 + 16 + 25 = 42$$
$$16 + 4 = 20$$
$$4 + 0 = 4$$
$$16$$
$$1 + 36 = 37$$

So 37, 58, 89, 145, 42, 20 and 4 are SAD

The HAPPY NUMBERS up to 100 are:

1	10	23	31	44		68	70	82	91
7	13	28	32	49			79	86	94
	19								97
									100

The other numbers are SAD.

DARTS

1 - DART SCORES

SINGLE	1	2	3	4	5	6	7	8	9	10	11	12
DOUBLES	2	4	6	8	10	12	14	16	18	20	22	24
TREBLES	3	6	9	12	15	18	21	24	27	30	33	36

So, all numbers up to 36 are possible, except:
13, 17, 19, 23, 25, 26, 28, 29, 31, 32, 34, 35.

2-DART SCORES

Score	Throws	Score	Throws	Score	Throws
1		25	D 12, S1	49	
2	S1, S1	26	D 12, S2	50	T12, D7
3	S2, S1	27	T8, S3	51	T12, T5
4	S3, S1	28	T9, S1	52	T12, D8
5	S4, S1	29	T9, S2	53	
6	S5, S1	30	T6, T4	54	T12, D9
7	S6, S1	31	T10, S1	55	
8	S7, S1	32	T10, S2	56	T12, D10
9	S8, S1	33	T10, S3	57	T12, T7
10	S9, S1	34	T11, S1	58	T12, D11
11	S10, S1	35	T11, S2	59	
12	S11, S1	36	T11, S3	60	T12, D12
13	S12, S1	37	T12, S1	61	
14	D3, D4	38	T12, S2	62	
15	T4, S3	39	T12, S3	63	T12, T9
16	D6, D2	40	T12, D2	64	
17	D8, D1	41	T12, S5	65	
18	D8, S2	42	T12, D3	66	T12, T10
19	D9, S1	43	T12, S7	67	
20	D9, S2	44	T12, D4	68	
21	T6, T1	45	T12, S9	69	T12, T11
22	D10, D1	46	T12, D5	70	
23	D 11, S1	47	T12, S11	71	
24	D 11, S2	48	T12, D6	72	T12, T12

ANGLING

The angles are:

ANGLE	EXACT
1	162°
2	41°
3	67°
4	41°
5	97°
6	138°
7	233°
8	328°
9	21°
10	75°

BORED GAME

The impossible numbers are:

24	8	10	4	56	16	42
18	(22)	44	40	3	63	35
48	7	45	12	(25)	20	6
21	15	(30)	9	14	54	8

For designing your own game the possible products can be obtained from a multiplication table. The circled numbers are repeats.

X	3	4	5	7	8	9
1	3	4	5	7	8	9
2	6	(8)	10	14	16	18
3	(9)	12	15	21	24	27
4	(12)	(16)	20	28	32	36
5	(15)	(20)	25	35	40	45
6	(18)	(24)	30	42	48	54

So, there are 28 different numbers to fill the 28 spaces.

FOUR DIGITS

Here is one set of possible solutions:

1	2 − 1	16	21 − 5
2	5 − 2 − 1	17	15 + 2
3	5 − 2	18	6 × (·1 + 2)
4	6 − 2	19	25 − 6
5	6 − 1	20	5 × (6 − 2)
6	5 + 1	21	26 − 5
7	5 + 2	22	26 + 1 − 5
8	6 + 2	23	15 + 2 + 6
9	6 + 2 + 1	24	25 − 1
10	2 × 5	25	26 − 1
11	16 − 5	26	25 + 1
12	2 × 6	27	26 + 1
13	(2 × 6) + 1	28	56 ÷ 2
14	16 − 2	29	(5 × 6) − 1
15	21 − 6	30	5 × 6

SUMMING UP

The 12 possible answers are:

```
  24      23      23      32      31      41
  15      15      14      14      24      23
  36      46      56      56      56      56
+ 13    + 13    + 13    + 13    + 13    + 13
  88      97     106     115     124     133

  13      13      23      32      32      42
  42      42      41      41      51      51
  56      65      65      65      64      63
+ 31    + 31    + 31    + 31    + 31    + 31
 142     151     160     169     178     187
```

SHAPELY

Some of the shapes include:

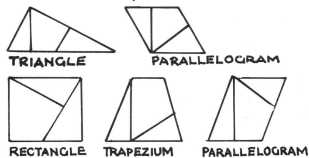

TRIANGLE   PARALLELOGRAM

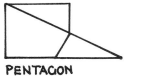

RECTANGLE   TRAPEZIUM   PARALLELOGRAM

PENTAGON   HEXAGON

TRIVIAL PURSUITS

If each pupil in the class makes 4 cards, and then all cards are collected together, the end result is enough cards for a game. Pupils could design a board for the game.

CASTLES

CASTLE 59

	59		
	31	28	
15	16	12	
6	9	7	5
1	5	4	3	2

CASTLE 58

	58		
	26	32	
10	16	16	
3	7	9	7
1	2	5	4	3

CASTLE 57

	57		
	29	28	
14	15	13	
6	8	7	6
1	5	3	4	2

CASTLE 56

	56		
	24	32	
9	15	17	
3	6	9	8
1	2	4	5	3

CASTLE 55

	55		
	25	30	
10	15	15	
3	7	8	7
1	2	5	3	4

CASTLE 53

	53		
	30	23	
16	14	9	
7	9	5	4
2	5	4	1	3

CASTLE 52

	52		
	25	27	
11	14	13	
5	6	8	5
4	1	5	3	2

CASTLE 51

	51		
	21	30	
8	13	17	
3	5	8	9
1	2	3	5	4

CASTLE 50

	50		
	28	22	
15	13	9	
8	7	6	3
5	3	4	2	1

CASTLE 54 is impossible.

DIVISORS

	DIVISORS	Total		DIVISORS	Total
1	1	1	26	1, 2, 13, 26	4
2	1, 2	2	27	1, 3, 9, 27	4
3	1, 3	2	28	1, 2, 4, 7, 14, 28	6
4	1, 2, 4	3	29	1, 29	2
5	1, 5	2	30	1, 2, 3, 5, 6, 10, 15, 30	8
6	1, 2, 3, 6	4	31	1, 31	2
7	1, 7	2	32	1, 2, 4, 8, 16, 32	6
8	1, 2, 4, 8	4	33	1, 3, 11, 33	4
9	1, 3, 9	3	34	1, 2, 17, 34	4
10	1, 2, 5, 10	4	35	1, 5, 7, 35	4
11	1, 11	2	36	1, 2, 3, 4, 6, 9, 12, 18, 36	9
12	1, 2, 3, 4, 6, 12	6	37	1, 37	2
13	1, 13	2	38	1, 2, 19, 38	4
14	1, 2, 7, 14	4	39	1, 3, 13, 39	4
15	1, 3, 5, 15	4	40	1, 2, 4, 5, 8, 10, 20, 40	8
16	1, 2, 4, 8, 16	5	41	1, 41	2
17	1, 17	2	42	1, 2, 3, 6, 7, 14, 21, 42	8
18	1, 2, 3, 6, 9, 18	6	43	1, 43	2
19	1, 19	2	44	1, 2, 4, 11, 22, 44	6
20	1, 2, 4, 5, 10, 20	6	45	1, 3, 5, 9, 15, 45	6
21	1, 3, 7, 21	4	46	1, 2, 23, 46	4
22	1, 2, 11, 22	4	47	1, 47	2
23	1, 23	2	48	1, 2, 3, 4, 6, 8, 12, 16, 24, 48	10
24	1, 2, 3, 4, 6, 8, 12, 24	8	49	1, 7, 49	3
25	1, 5, 25	3	50	1, 2, 5, 10, 25, 50	6

NUMBERS WITH 2 DIVISORS are prime numbers.
3 DIVISORS are square numbers.

TRIANGLES

The 20 different Triangles are :

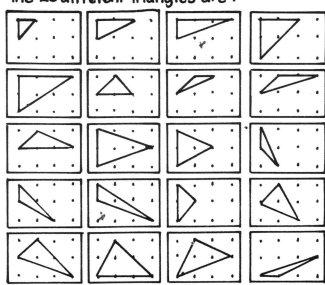

CALENDARS

$$\bigcirc \times \bigcirc = 160$$
$$\diamondsuit \times \diamondsuit = \underline{132}$$

DIFFERENCE   28

The difference is always 28 since

a	a + 1	a + 2
a + 7	a + 8	a + 9
a + 14	a + 15	a + 16

$$\bigcirc \times \bigcirc = (a+2)(a+14)$$
$$= a^2 + 16a + 28$$
$$\diamondsuit \times \diamondsuit = a(a+16)$$
$$= a^2 + 16a$$

DIFFERENCE   28

This activity provides an interesting illustration of the manipulation of algebraic expressions.

DAVID'S HOMEWORK

①
```
   35
  ×42
 1400
   70
 1470 ✓
```

②
```
   28
  ×46
 1120
  168
 1288 ✓
```

③
```
   16
  ×43
  640
   64
  704 ✓
```

④
```
   54
  × 38
 1620
  4⑤2
 2072 ✗
```

⑤
```
   36
  ×27
  720
  252
  972 ✓
```

⑥
```
   72
  ×51
 3600
   72
 3672 ✓
```

⑦
```
   73
  ×44
 2920
  292
 3212 ✓
```

⑧
```
   67
  × 29
 1340
  6①3
 1953 ✗
```

⑨
```
   82
  ×19
  820
  6③8
 1458 ✗
```

⑩
```
   49
  ×37
 1470
  343
 1813 ✓
```

7/10

SIGNS

① $(9 + 3) \times 2 = 24$
② $5 \times (4 + 6) = 50$
③ $7 \times (5 - 2) = 21$
④ $(8 - 5) \times 4 = 12$
⑤ $(6 + 3) \times 7 = 63$
⑥ $(5 + 4) \times (6 - 1) = 45$
⑦ $5 + (6 \times 2) - 3 = 14$
⑧ $7 + 5 + (4 \times 3) = 24$
⑨ $9 - 3 + (6 \times 5) = 36$
⑩ $(8 - 2) \times (5 - 1) = 24$

SUNSHINE AND RAIN

Possible solutions include

A a) BIRMINGHAM (8·5) SOUTHPORT (6·5)
  b) BRISTOL (7·8) BUXTON (6·8)
  c) GLASGOW (3·6) LONDON (5·1)
  d) ABERDEEN (1·0) CARLISLE (4·5)
  e) MANCHESTER (5·2) WICK (2·9)

B a) DUNBAR (0·44) PRESTWICK (0·14)
  b) LEEDS (0·07) MANCHESTER (0·27)
  c) LONDON (0·33) KINLOSS (0·18)
  d) PRESTWICK (0·14) TIREE (0·19)
  e) NORWICH (0·08) CARLISLE (0·16)

SWEET SEVENTEEN

The seventeen polygons are:

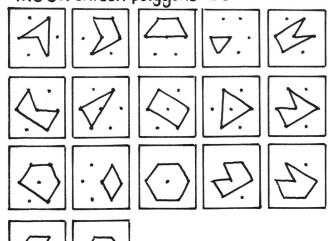

MASTERMIND

Pupils inventions of ten questions can be used as test questions to be tried out on the whole class.

The answers to "ANGLES" are:

1. PROTRACTOR
2. $90°$
3. ACUTE
4. $225°$
5. $30°, 60°, 90°$ OR $45°, 45°, 90°$
6. $60°$
7. $59°$
8. $45°$
9. $6°$
10. $35°, 35°$

CLUELESS

1)

5	3	4	12
8	2	6	16
7	1	9	17
20	6	19	

2)

8	9	4	21
6	7	2	15
5	3	1	9
19	19	7	

3)

5	1	4	10
7	6	8	21
3	2	9	14
15	9	21	

4)

3	5	6	14
2	8	9	19
1	4	7	12
6	17	22	

5)

4	2	7	13
5	3	8	16
6	1	9	16
15	6	24	

6)

8	7	3	18
5	6	9	20
1	4	2	7
14	17	14	

Pupils will find these puzzles easier if they have a set of nine cards numbered 1 – 9. The cards can then be moved around in the search for the correct solution.

THINK TANK

These two puzzles result in the number first thought of.
They provide valuable practice in the handling of algebraic expressions.

RECTANGLES

CORNER SUM 35

1	2	3	4
11	12	13	14
21	22	23	24
31	32	33	34

5	6	7	8	9	10
15	16	17	18	19	20
25	26	27	28	29	30

6	7	8	9
16	17	18	19
26	27	28	29

11	12	13	14
21	22	23	24

12	13
22	23

7	8
17	18
27	28

CORNER SUM 50
Eight rectangles are possible.

1	2	3	4	5	6	7	8	9
11	12	13	14	15	16	17	18	19
21	22	23	24	25	26	27	28	29
31	32	33	34	35	36	37	38	39
41	42	43	44	45	46	47	48	49

2	3	4	5	6	7	8
12	13	14	15	16	17	18
22	23	24	25	26	27	28
32	33	34	35	36	37	38
42	43	44	45	46	47	48

3	4	5	6	7
13	14	15	16	17
23	24	25	26	27
33	34	35	36	37
43	44	45	46	47

4	5	6
14	15	16
24	25	26
34	35	36
44	45	46

12	13	14	15	16	17	18
22	23	24	25	26	27	28
32	33	34	35	36	37	38

13	14	15	16	17
23	24	25	26	27
33	34	35	36	37

11	12	13	14	15	16	17	18	19
21	22	23	24	25	26	27	28	29
31	32	33	34	35	36	37	38	39

14	15	16
24	25	26
34	35	36

SWAPPO

16 MOVES ⬆   20 MOVES ⬇

THE GREAT DIVIDE

Several different arrangements will produce the same maximum score.

SIGNPOSTS

Some possible solutions are :

	SET OF NUMBERS	TARGET	EXPRESSION	SCORE
1	3 4 5 6 8	4	(6÷3)+(8÷4)	9
2	5 6 7 1 2	5	(6×2)-(7×1)	8
3	3 8 5 9 2	3	5-(9-8)-(3-2)	8
4	2 3 4 6 7	8	34 - 26	2
5	4 5 3 2 6	7	(32÷4)+5-6	7
6	1 3 5 7 9	2	(9÷3)+5+1-7	8
7	2 4 6 8 3	9	(8÷2)+6+3-4	9
8	4 6 8 5 9	20	5×4	3
				54

CONSECUTIVES

The powers of 2 are impossible.

1		21	10+11
2		22	4+5+6+7
3	1+2	23	11+12
4		24	7+8+9
5	2+3	25	12+13
6	1+2+3	26	5+6+7+8
7	3+4	27	13+14
8		28	1+2+3+4+5+6+7
9	4+5	29	14+15
10	1+2+3+4	30	9+10+11
11	5+6	31	15+16
12	3+4+5	32	
13	6+7	33	16+17
14	2+3+4+5	34	7+8+9+10
15	7+8	35	17+18
16		36	11+12+13
17	8+9	37	18+19
18	5+6+7	38	8+9+10+11
19	9+10	39	19+20
20	2+3+4+5+6	40	6+7+8+9+10

AROUND THE WORLD

An interesting project for the pupils would be to monitor the temperatures of ten cities over a period of weeks or months. Graphs can then be drawn to represent seasonal temperature changes.

ODD, EVEN, PRIME

A possible solution is:

	2,3,8	5,1,4	3,6,4
ODD NUMBER	28 + 3	4 + 1	6 + 3
EVEN NUMBER	28	5 - 1	6 + 4
PRIME NUMBER BETWEEN 10 AND 40	23	14 + 5	43 - 6
PRIME NUMBER BETWEEN 50 AND 100	83	54 - 1	63 - 4
SQUARE NUMBER	3 - 2	4	3 + 6
CUBE NUMBER	8	5 + 4 - 1	64
DIVISOR OF 36	8 - 2	5 + 4	36
TRIANGULAR NUMBER	38 - 2	5 + 4 + 1	12 - 6
NUMBER LESS THAN 12	8 + 3	5 + 1	6 - 4 + 3
NUMBER MORE THAN 60	82	51 × 4	63
NUMBER BETWEEN 10 AND 20	23 - 8	14	3 × 4
MULTIPLE OF 3	8 - 3 - 2	51	4 × 6
MULTIPLE OF 4	2^3	4^5	4 × 6 × 3
MULTIPLE OF 5	83 + 2	45	36 + 4

MIDDLIN'

2, 3, 4, 5, 7, 9 : 18 different MIDDLE numbers are possible.

```
34   35   37   39
42   43   45   47   49
52   53   54   57   59
72   73   74   75
```

3, 3, 4, 5, 5, 8 : 8 different MIDDLE numbers are possible.

```
35   38
43   45   48
53   54   55
```

BALANCING ACTS

1. $4 \oplus 9 \oplus 3 = 16$
2. $5 \oplus 8 \ominus 3 = 10$
3. $6 \ominus 2 \ominus 1 = 3$
4. $9 \ominus 6 \oplus 8 = 11$
5. $6 \ominus 1 \oplus 4 = 9$
6. $6 \oplus 7 \oplus 8 \ominus 2 = 19$
7. $5 \oplus 4 \ominus 3 \oplus 1 = 7$
8. $6 \ominus 3 \ominus 5 \oplus 2 = 0$
9. $4 \ominus 4 \oplus 6 \oplus 1 = 7$
10. $9 \oplus 3 \ominus 7 \ominus 1 = 4$

KNIGHTY KNIGHT

Some possible solutions are:

1.
	3	6	
1	8	11	4
10	5	2	7
	12	9	

2.
1	4	7	10
12	9	2	5
3	6	11	8

3.
1	20	7	16	3
6	15	2	11	8
19	10	13	4	17
14	5	18	9	12

4.
1	14	9	20	3
24	19	2	15	10
13	8	25	4	21
18	23	6	11	16
7	12	17	22	5

5.
1	32	9	22	7	30
10	23	36	31	16	21
33	2	17	8	29	6
24	11	26	35	20	15
3	34	13	18	5	28
12	25	4	27	14	19

MISPRINTS

The sets are:

$$\frac{1}{2} \quad \frac{2}{4} \quad \frac{3}{6} \quad \frac{4}{8}$$

$$\frac{1}{4} \quad \frac{2}{8} \quad \frac{3}{12} \quad \frac{4}{16}$$

$$\frac{3}{4} \quad \frac{6}{8} \quad \frac{9}{12}$$

$$\frac{2}{3} \quad \frac{4}{6} \quad \frac{6}{9} \quad \frac{8}{12}$$

$$\frac{1}{5} \quad \frac{2}{10} \quad \frac{3}{15} \quad \frac{4}{20}$$

$$\frac{3}{5} \quad \frac{6}{10} \quad \quad \frac{12}{20}$$

$$\frac{4}{5} \quad \frac{8}{10} \quad \frac{12}{15} \quad \frac{16}{20}$$

$$\frac{1}{6} \quad \frac{2}{12} \quad \frac{3}{18} \quad \frac{4}{24}$$

$$\frac{5}{6} \quad \frac{10}{12} \quad \frac{15}{18} \quad \frac{20}{24}$$

$$\frac{1}{8} \quad \frac{2}{16} \quad \frac{3}{24} \quad \frac{4}{32}$$

The MISPRINTS are $\frac{8}{20}$ and $\frac{6}{16}$

EXCEPTIONS

1. | 4 | 8 | 11 |

    4, 8, 11 have area 6 units^2
    All the others have area 5 units^2

2. | 6 | 11 | 14 |

    6 has perimeter 10 units.
    8 and 11 have perimeter 14 units.
    All the others have perimeter 12 units.

3. | 2 | 4 | 5 | 9 | 12 | 14 |

    2, 4, 5, 9, 12 and 14 have 8 sides.
    1, 6, 10 have   6 sides
    7, 8 13 have   10 sides
    3, 11   have   12 sides

4. | 3 | 7 | 10 | 14 | 12 |

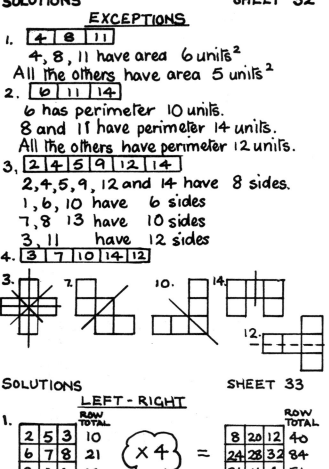

LEFT - RIGHT

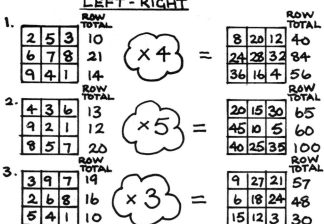

PHASES

	ANAGRAM	SHAPE
1	RECLIC	CIRCLE
2	ONCE	CONE
3	GOATNOC	OCTAGON
4	DIMPRAY	PYRAMID
5	CANDORHODDEE	DODECAHEDRON
6	QUEARS	SQUARE
7	SMIRP	PRISM
8	NIGLERAT	TRIANGLE
9	SHODICONARE	ICOSAHEDRON
10	NAPGOTEN	PENTAGON
11	REPESH	SPHERE
12	GALLOPMARRELA	PARALLELOGRAM
13	ROTTENHEARD	TETRAHEDRON
14	CONDAGE	DECAGON
15	BUEC	CUBE
16	LECTGRANE	RECTANGLE
17	ROLYPHONED	POLYHEDRON
18	TIKE	KITE
19	CHAREOTOND	OCTAHEDRON
20	SHURBOM	RHOMBUS
21	DRINCLEY	CYLINDER
22	AQUATIDELLARR	QUADRILATERAL
23	BODICU	CUBOID
24	NAXEHOG	HEXAGON
25	REATIZUMP	TRAPEZIUM

CROSSPATCH

Some possible solutions include:

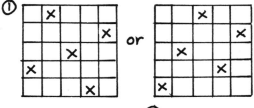

①   or

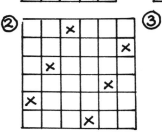

②   ③

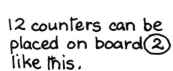

12 counters can be
placed on board ②
like this.

BILLS

7p :	5p, 2p
13p :	10p, 2p, 1p
11p :	10p, 1p
18p :	10p, 5p, 2p, 1p
14p :	IMPOSSIBLE
17p :	10p, 5p, 2p
12p :	10p, 2p
15p :	10p, 5p
9p :	IMPOSSIBLE
16p :	10p, 5p, 1p

5p, 10p, 20p and a 50p coin will pay these bills :

5p, 10p, 15p, 20p, 25p, 30p, 35p, 50p, 55p, 60p, 70p, 75p, 80p, 85p.

BIG AITCH

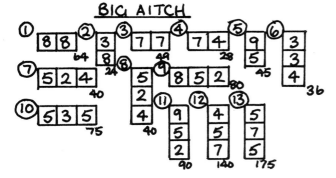

FIND FIVE

Some possible solutions are :

	(32)	(23)	(16)
1	4 × 8	24 − 1	14 + 2
2	24 + 8	18 + 5	12 + 4
3	84 − 52	28 − 5	18 − 2
4	28 + 4	15 + 8	8 × 2
5	2^5	(48 ÷ 2) − 1	8 + 5 + 3 + 1

SHADASHAPE

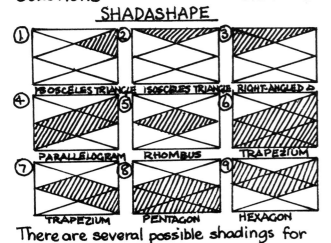

There are several possible shadings for most of these shapes.

TENSION

The 10 shapes are :

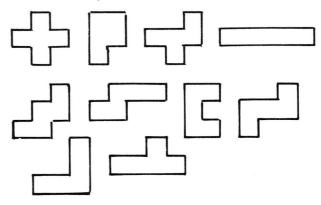

SUBNORMAL

The 12 different answers are :

8, 12, 15, 19, 21, 25, 26, 34, 37, 43, 48, 52

65	65	63	63	61	61
−13	−31	−51	−15	−35	−53
52	34	12	48	26	8

56	56	53	51	36	35
−31	−13	−16	−36	−15	−16
25	43	37	15	21	19

HAT-TRICKS

Ⓐ 13, 23, 31, 41, 43, 53
Ⓑ 29, 67, 79, 89, 97
Ⓒ 13, 17, 31, 37, 61, 67, 71, 73, 83
Ⓓ 13, 17, 31, 37, 41, 43, 47, 53, 71, 73

The five numbers 1, 3, 4, 7, 9 lead to :

13, 17, 19, 31, 37, 41, 43, 47, 71, 73, 79, 97

SATISFACTION

One possible solution is :

	EVEN NUMBERS	MULTIPLES OF 2	ODD NUMBERS	PRIME NUMBERS
NUMBERS BETWEEN 11 AND 18	16	14	15	13
NUMBERS LESS THAN 12	8	10	7	11
FACTORS OF 36	12	6	9	3
NUMBERS LESS THAN 7	2	4	1	5

SIDE-SPLITTERS

Possible solutions include :

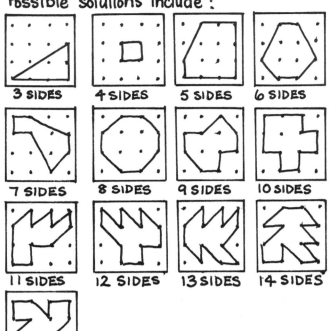

3 SIDES   4 SIDES   5 SIDES   6 SIDES

7 SIDES   8 SIDES   9 SIDES   10 SIDES

11 SIDES   12 SIDES   13 SIDES   14 SIDES

15 SIDES

ENTRIES

Possible entries include :

	UNITS OF MEASUREMENT	SHAPES
A	ACRE	ARROWHEAD
C	CENTIMETRE	CIRCLE
D	DECIMETRE	DECAGON
E	ELL	EQUILATERAL TRIANGLE
F	FOOT	FLEXAGON
G	GRAM	GREEK CROSS
H	HECTARE	HEXAGON
I	INCH	ISOSCELES TRIANGLE
K	KILOMETRE	KITE
L	LITRE	LOOP
N	NAUTICAL MILE	NONAGON
O	OUNCE	OCTAGON
P	PINT	PARALLELOGRAM
Q	QUART	QUADRILATERAL
R	ROOD	RECTANGLE
S	SECOND	SQUARE
T	TON	TRIANGLE

FILL-INS

①	3	5	8	13	21	34
②	4	9	13	22	35	57
③	4	5	9	14	23	37
④	3	4	7	11	18	29
⑤	5	6	11	17	28	45
⑥	6	7	13	20	33	53
⑦	2	3	5	8	13	21

PAIRS

TOTAL OF 9.

TOTAL OF 10.

Impossible totals : 4 , 15

CORNER NUMBERS

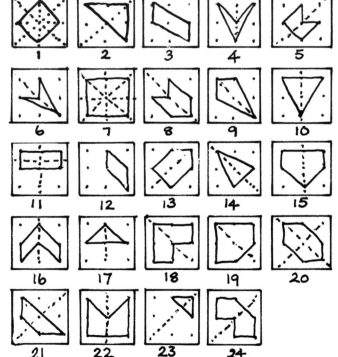

SYMMETRY

1   2   3   4   5

6   7   8   9   10

11   12   13   14   15

16   17   18   19   20

21   22   23   24

3 and 12 have no lines of symmetry.

Shapes 1, 7, 11 and 20 have more than one line of symmetry.

These each have rotational symmetry.